What's worse than
a giraffe with a sore throat?
A hippopotamus with chapped lips

Why did Humpty Dumpty
have a great fall?
To make up for a rotten summer.

How do you make gold stew?
Add fourteen carrots.

You'll be laughing all the way through
Sonny Fox's funny, foxy joke book,
FUNNIER THAN THE FIRST ONE.

FUNNIER
than the first one

a new joke book by
SONNY FOX

drawings by
BOB GRAY

A BERKLEY MEDALLION BOOK
PUBLISHED BY
BERKLEY PUBLISHING CORPORATION

G. P. Putnam's Sons
200 Madison Avenue
New York, New York 10022

Library of Congress Catalog Card Number: 70-189883

SBN 425-02536-5

BERKLEY MEDALLION BOOKS are published by
Berkley Publishing Corporation
200 Madison Avenue
New York, N.Y. 10016

BERKLEY MEDALLION BOOKS ® TM 757,375

Printed in the United States of America

Berkley Medallion Edition, April, 1974

Contents

Funnier Than the First One   9

Riddles   17

Shaggy Fox Tales   33

Jokes Elephants Tell   39

Way-Out Jokes   47

Tongue Depressing   57

Oddballs and Common Squares   63

Frantic Antics   71

Daffy-Dillies   81

Clues Closet   91

Funnier Than the
First One

Funnier Than the First One

Here's a new collection of riddles, puns, stories and jokes for your reading pleasure. But most of all, they should be for your telling pleasure. It's like the out-of-towner who passed the street violinist outside the Empire State Building. Being lost, he asked the violinist, "How do I get to Carnegie Hall?" and the violinist answered, "Practice, my son, practice!"

There were tips in my first book, *Jokes and How to Tell Them*, about how to tell jokes. Well, I've added some more: First, know your jokes—be able to tell them without forgetting any of the important parts or punch line. By knowing your jokes you can stay on one subject and tell one, two or three jokes about the same thing. If you do this and then switch over to another subject and tell a few more jokes, then you will find you are building a routine. This is what successful comedians do. Next time you watch a top comedian, listen carefully to his routine. You will see that he stays on one subject for a time and then eases into another.

To be a good joke teller you must have a large source of stories at your command. Friends will get tired of hearing the same stories over and over again. It pays to write jokes down. Start your own gag file by clipping them out of newspapers and magazines. Just be sure to ask your parents about this first, or else it might not be funny—for you.

Perhaps you could buy some of the comedy records by some of the funny comedians you like so you can hear how they emphasize a story. Get them anywhere, but start your own joke file, with notes on how to tell them. This will serve two purposes.

One, you will be amazed at how fast your file can grow. Two, after a while you can see the same joke repeated, updated and changed to fit new situations. You can learn a great deal from your joke file.

Your public library will have many books on jokes, puns, riddles, toastmaster stories, etc. They usually are found in one section. Look them up under "Humor," or ask your librarian to help you. If one book is particularly good, you may want to order it from your local bookstore. Let's not overlook this as a prime source for your own gag file. Like a carpenter or plumber, you need tools to practice joke-telling. Jokes are your tools, and they should be polished and available when you need them. You should have a good supply.

Practicing jokes means *telling* them, not in front of a mirror, but to others. One comedian I know writes the punch lines of jokes on a small card that he carries with him in the breast pocket of his suit. By glancing

quickly at the card, it triggers his mind and then he tells the whole joke. This is a very good method for recalling jokes. (In a bathing suit he's very unfunny.)

In time you might start jotting down jokes you've heard during the day. Carry a small notebook with you. Again, you'll be astounded how fast you can fill it up.

Another tip for joke telling: Be careful of the words you use. Don't kill a joke by tipping the audience off to the punch line. Take the following joke: "Why did the boy put a firecracker under his *stack of* pancakes? He wanted to blow his *stack*!" Now look what happens when you leave the words "stack of" out of the first line. You have the element of surprise. Your audience gets the connection, and the play on the word "stack" is funny.

In a pun-type joke never use the word in the punch line that the gag hangs on in the beginning of the joke. This is a common mistake of which poor joke tellers are often guilty. You lose the whole effect—and your audience too.

While we're at it, how many times has this happened at a joke-telling session: One person is telling a story: "Did I tell you that my grandfather put wheels on his rocking chair? Now he can rock and roll!" And then someone else pipes up: "I heard that one differently. It goes: " 'Did you hear Whistler's mother is missing? She's off her rocker!' " Now both those jokes are funny, but both use the same idea and play on the same word. The second joke teller didn't get much of a laugh. He should have saved the gag for a later time.

At a party, never tell the same story someone else has, no matter how differently it starts, if the endings are basically the same.

Through the years there's been another invaluable lesson that I've learned about jokes and people. You all know the person who stops a joke teller after the first sentence with that killer: "I've heard it." In show business I've yet to hear any top comic I know use that line. There are a few simple reasons for this, the first being that jokes change so rapidly that even if the beginnings are similar, the endings may be vastly different. Someone along the way could have added something to make the joke funnier or perhaps someone left something out that was important. For example, I know this joke: "Why are you so sad?" "I waited all my life and finally saved enough money to achieve my one ambition. I went out and bought a solid-gold, non-magnetic, lifetime-guaranteed, shatterproof, rustproof, waterproof, battery-operated wristwatch." "What happened?" "I lost it."

The next week I heard it this way: "Why are you wearing that bandage on your wrist?" "Last week I finally saved enough money to buy one of those solid-state, nonmagnetic, lifetime-guaranteed, shatterproof, waterproof, battery-operated wristwatches." "What happened?" "It caught fire!" And yesterday someone told it to me like this: Two boys met on the street. "Why are you so sad?" asked the first boy. The second boy answered, "Yesterday was my birthday and my dad gave me a solid-state, nonmagnetic, lifetime-guaranteed, shatterproof, waterproof, battery-operated wristwatch." "That's great," said the first boy, "but why are you so sad?" And the second boy answered, "I can't tell time."

See what I mean? Same joke, but which one is funnier? Also remember, at a party or joke session no one likes the smart guy who knows all the jokes. You are depriving the audience of hearing a funny story with, "I've heard it." You'll probably read a lot of books on jokes, and they give valuable hints, but common courtesy and good manners mean *learning to be a good audience*. And as I've shown you, you may be missing a funny story that you have heard before but in a different way.

Now, if you are caught with someone who interrupts your joke and won't let you finish, he is what we will call the proverbial heckler. Try some of the "Rank Outs" I've put in this book. They may not exactly shut him up, but you can get some laughs with them. And they are humorous and not really offensive to the heckler. So who knows, he may even laugh at them himself. If you can zap him with a few, he may also

13

be at a loss for words, and, of course, you can then *finish* your interrupted story.

Another hint is to put that added touch to your stories which can get your audience in a chuckling mood. These are called "buildup" lines. For instance, in starting a cannibal joke, you might throw in: "The cannibal's wife was sitting there knitting a blowgun." It's short, humorous and doesn't detract from the story; rather, it adds to it. Look over the following: "He lived in a town so small they couldn't have a parade. There wouldn't be anyone to watch it." "The Indian chief named Running Water had two daughters, Hot and Cold, and a son named Luke." "On the farm he heard 'oom oom,' but it was just a cow walking backward." "Then he went to a hospital, where people who are run down wind up and. . . ." "About four thousand years ago, on a Friday. . . ." "This is a myth, which you all know is a female moth."

These and others, which are short one-liners or jokes within themselves, can be combined or inserted into jokes to make them funnier. Be on the lookout for these shorties, for they are used by many comedians to build a joke. Don't overdo it, though, as these should not take away from the main punch line. Many of these one-liners could be used alone, but not with as much impact as they have when you make them a part of a longer story.

I've separated the jokes in this book into different sections. As in my first book, they follow a pattern, so if you decide to retell them, you'll have a few that can be strung together. I've had fun putting them down for you, and I hope you have as much fun reading them, so now

14

Funnier Than the First One

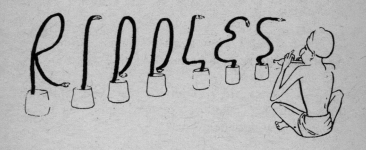

Ever since Oedipus answered the riddle of the Sphinx, men have been fascinated by riddles. Riddle of the Sphinx: What animal is it that in the morning goes on four feet, at noon on two, and in the evening upon three? Oedipus answered: Man, who in childhood creeps on hands and knees, in manhood walks erect, and in old age with the aid of a cane. Over the centuries the words have been changed to reflect the changes in the language and the mores of the people. They continually adapt themselves to the things of our everyday life. "What do you do when hot pants catch fire?" "You get the panty hose." Couldn't have been told ten years ago, but it is timely today.

Read these riddles from the year 1930:

Q. Which one of our Presidents wore the largest shoes?
A. The one with the largest feet.

Q. What's the left part of a cake?
A. The side that has not been eaten.

Q. Why did Adam bite the apple Eve gave him?
A. He didn't have a knife to cut it with.

Q. If a lady falls, why can't her brother help her?
A. How could he be a brother and assist her too?

These riddles are still around, but you don't hear them as often. Today we are much more apt to hear some of the following:

Q. What's brown and green and crawls through the grass?
A. A Girl Scout and a Brownie looking for a lost cookie.

Q. How do they play Russian roulette in India?
A. You play the flute with six cobras around you and one of them is deaf.

Q. What does the nearsighted Gingerbread Man use for eyes?
A. Contact raisins.

We put into our 1970 riddles the now things. Riddles are sillier and funnier and less in the way of the old-fashioned mental exercises of our forefathers. In every country children tell riddles, and right now I'm sure some young lad in London just thought up a new one.

Maybe he will send it to me. So here goes for more and merrier riddles:

Q. What is the main job of the President?
A. Cabinetmaking.

Q. What do you get if you cross a kangaroo with a 747?
A. A kangaroo that shows movies in its pouch.

Q. What else do you get if you cross a kangaroo with a 747?
A. A plane that makes short hops.

Q. What is a hospital for parrots called?
A. A polly clinic.

Q. Who invented the grandfather clock?
A. Pendulum Franklin.

Q. What did the hippie say to the invisible man?
A. Hey, tough man, you're out of sight.

Q. What's red and goes up and down?
A. A tomato in an elevator.

Q. What happened when the canary flew into a blender?
A. Shredded tweet.

Q. What's the difference between a teacher and a train?
A. The teacher says, "Get rid of your gum," and the train says, "Chew chew!"

Q. Why did the soldier salute the refrigerator?
A. Because it was General Electric.

Q. What is a bull when it's sleeping?
A. A bulldozer.

Q. What do you get when you cross a porcupine with a sheep?
A. An animal that knits its own sweaters. (Get the point?)

Q. What has four legs and flies?
A. A picnic table.

Q. Why couldn't anyone play cards on Noah's Ark?
A. Because Noah was always standing on the deck.

Q. If that's a watchdog, how come he's running around in circles?
A. He's all wound up.

Q. What happened to the girl who didn't know the difference between cold cream and putty?
A. All her windows fell out, and her face had a funny glaze.

Q. What did Snow White say when her pictures did not arrive back from the photo service?
A. Someday my prints will come.

Q. How do you drive a baby buggy?
A. Tickle its feet.

Q. Why was the house empty?
A. The fire had gone out, the eggs had scrambled, the cards had cut, the rope had skipped, and the stockings had run.

Q. Why did the hippie have a ringing in his ears?
A. His bell-bottom pants were too tight.

Q. What is the definition of a junkyard?
A. A Chinese harbor.

Q. What colors would you paint the sun and the wind?
A. The sun rose and the wind blew.

Q. What keeps the moon from falling?
A. Its beams, of course.

Q. What did the lollipop say to the wrapper?
A. Stick to me or I'm licked.

Q. What Roman numeral grows?
A. IV.

Q. Why did the rocket lose its job?
A. It was fired.

Q. What did the dirt say when it rained?
A. If this keeps up, my name is mud.

Q. What is never used unless it is in a tight place?
A. A cork.

Q. What did Papa Lightning Bug say to Mama Lightning Bug?
A. Isn't Junior bright for his age?

Q. How do you stop a charging lion?
A. Take away his credit card.

Q. What did the vegetable say when it was wrapped up and put in the refrigerator the third night in a row?
A. Curses, foiled again.

Q. If all the cars in the nation were pink, what would we have?
A. A pink carnation.

Q. What do you get when you cross a sheep with a kangaroo?
A. Woolen jumpers.

Q. How do you catch a squirrel?
A. Run up a tree and act like a nut.

Q. What goes "foow, foow"?
A. A backward dog.

Q. What does the government use when it takes a census of all the monkeys in Kenya?
A. An ape recorder.

Q. What do they call the cabs lined up at the Dallas airport?
A. The yellow rows of taxis.

Q. What do you call a pharaoh who eats crackers in bed?
A. A crummy mummy.

Q. Why should you never mention the number 288 in polite company?
A. Because it is too (two) gross.

Q. Why did the two Indians' father put them in the yacht club?
A. He wanted to see his red sons in the sail set.

Q. Why did Humpty Dumpty have a great fall?
A. To make up for a rotten summer.

Q. What's the difference between a jeweler and a jailer?
A. One sells watches, and one watches cells.

Q. What's worse than a giraffe with a sore throat?
A. A hippopotamus with chapped lips.

Q. When do people say a farmer is good in his work?
A. When he's "out-standing" in his field.

Q. What two letters of the alphabet do children like best?
A. *C* and *Y*.

Q. Why was the rooster called Robinson?
A. Because he Crusoe.

Q. Why is a yo-yo like getting up at 4 A.M.?
A. It's twirly.

Q. Where is Minute Street?
A. 62d.

Q. Why are feet like ancient stories?
A. They're legends.

Q. What goes from Los Angeles to Chicago without moving?
A. Route 66.

Q. How do you make gold stew?
A. Add fourteen carrots.

Q. What do you call two people riding bikes together?
A. Cyclamates.

Q. Why is the Statue of Liberty's nose only eleven inches long?
A. If it were twelve inches long, it would be a foot.

Q. What's gray on the inside and clear on the outside?
A. An elephant in a baggie.

Q. What did one horse say to the other?
A. I can't seem to remember your mane, but your pace is familiar.

Q. What did one Moslem say to the other?
A. I can't seem to remember your name, but your fez is familiar.

Q. What is a tongue twister?
A. It's when your tang gets all tongueled up.

Q. What do spooks like at the amusement park?
A. The roller ghoster.

Q. What do you keep after giving it to someone?
A. A promise.

Q. What is it that everybody in the world is doing at the same time?
A. Growing older.

Q. What's the difference between a man parking his car and a man smashing dishes?
A. One sets the brake and the other breaks the set.

Q. Why didn't they want the human cannonball at the circus to quit?
A. They couldn't find another man of his calibre.

Q. Why do elephants drink so much?
A. To forget.

Q. What do you get if you cross a chicken with an elephant?
A. I don't know, but Colonel Sanders had a lot of trouble trying to dip it into the batter.

Q. Why did Santa use only seven reindeer last year?
A. Comet stayed home to take care of the sink.

Q. Why was the ink drop sad?
A. His father was in the pen and he didn't know how long the sentence would be. (His friend, the blotter, found that very absorbing.)

Q. Why doesn't a Volkswagen have to pay a bridge toll?
A. The driver pays it.

Q. What's a small joke called?
A. A mini-ha-ha.

Q. If a dog lost his tail, where would he get another one?
A. At the retail store, naturally.

Q. What is the main reason for using a cookie sheet?
A. For cookies to sleep on.

Q. What international catastrophe would be caused by a waiter's dropping the meat platter on Thanksgiving?
A. The downfall of Turkey and the destruction of China.

Q. Why does the moon go to the bank?
A. To change its quarters.

Q. What did one shrub say to the other?
A. Boy, am I bushed.

Q. What has twenty heads but can't think?
A. A matchbook.

Q. What is a twip?
A. A twip is what a wabbit takes when he wides a twain.

Q. If a man died in England who was born in China, reared in France, worked in America, and married in Brazil, what is he?
A. Dead.

Q. Three potato chips were on the Golden Gate Bridge. One jumped off. Why didn't the other two jump?
A. They were Wise Potato Chips.

Q. What's the best way to prevent disease caused by biting insects?
A. Don't bite any.

Q. What can travel around the world and still stay in one corner?
A. A postage stamp.

Q. Why does the ocean roar?
A. You would too if you had lobsters in your bed.

Q. What is the least dangerous kind of robbery?
A. A safe robbery.

Q. How does a ghost eat?
A. By goblin.

Q. What's the difference between the South Pole and the North Pole?
A. All the difference in the world.

Q. If Rumpelstiltskin likes to sit on gold, who sits on silver?
A. The Lone Ranger.

Q. What goes around your house and never comes in?
A. A fence.

Q. What is it if when you pick it up you can move, but put it down and you both stay?
A. An anchor.

Q. What is lower with a head than without one?
A. A pillow.

Q. When was money invented?
A. When Adam got a greenback lying in the Garden of Eden.

Q. What disasters happen every twenty-four hours?
A. Day breaks and night falls.

Q. What happens if you sit on a grape?
A. It gives out a little wine.

Q. Why are the garden birds so sad this morning?
A. Because their bills are all over dew.

Q. Why is a coward like a leaky faucet?
A. They both run.

Q. What goes up into the air white and comes down yellow and white?
A. An egg.

Q. What stays hot in the refrigerator?
A. Mustard.

Q. What happens when two bullets get married?
A. They have a BB.

Q. How do you milk a caterpillar?
A. First, you get a low stool. . . .

Q. What is the greatest surgical operation on record?
A. Lancing Michigan.

Q. Why is a keyhole beautiful?
A. Because it's something to adore.

Q. What happens if you cross a camel with a cow?
A. You get a six-month supply of milk, but you need a ladder to milk it from the top.

Q. What is green, has two legs, and a trunk?
A. A seasick tourist.

Q. What goes "clomp, clomp, clomp, swish; clomp, clomp, clomp, swish"?
A. An elephant with a wet sneaker.

Shaggy Fox Tales

These are some of my favorites. The play on words in the punch lines gives the twist that catches your listener by surprise. They rely on common phrases that are familiar in everyday conversation but for the purpose of the joke are put into ridiculous situations.

Mike Custer decided to make his fortune selling hot dogs. He bought a frankfurter wagon, and by working twelve hours a day he prospered. Then he bought another wagon, and another. Everywhere people began to notice Michael Custer's Hot Dog Wagons. They became familiar all over the city. Suddenly misfortune struck. His business slowed down tremendously; he lost much money; and finally he had only one wagon left.

That was Custer's Last Stand.

BOB: I just read that famous book about seven turkeys.
ED: What book was that?
BOB: The House of the Seven Gobbles.

JACK: Did you hear about the tongue-tied rabbit who
　　　went to the dentist to get his tooth extracted?
BILL: No, what happened?
JACK: The dentist asked him if he wanted gas, and he
　　　said no because he was an ether bunny.

Finn and Huck were friends. Finn died. No one worried. They said: "Huck'll bury Finn."

Several famous chefs were eating at a monastery. The
dinner was fish and chips and was delicious. Wishing
to express their appreciation, the chefs asked the good
brothers of the monastery to direct them to the kitchen

so that they could pay their compliments to the chef. They went to the kitchen and, on seeing several workers, asked who had prepared their meal. "I'm the fish friar," said one man, "and that's the chip monk over there."

An English count and his helper had stolen the crown princess's jewels. The queen forced the count to admit it, but he refused to tell who his assistant was. The queen said, "Tell the name or you will be beheaded." He was silent. As he was being led to the chopping block, the count was asked again, but still he wouldn't tell. As the ax was coming down, the count yelled, "I'll tell I'll tell." Too late, however, for the ax fell.

The moral of this story is: Don't hatchet your counts before they chicken.

Remember this: Two wrongs don't make a right, but two Wrights made an airplane.

MAG: Did you know you can't send mail to Washington?
TOM: No, why can't I?
MAG: Because he's dead. But you can send mail to Lincoln.
TOM: But he's dead too.
MAG: I know, but he left his Gettysburg Address.

TINA: What's flat at the bottom, pointed at the top, and has ears?
MILLY: I give up.
TINA: A mountain.

MILLY: Oh, really—what about the ears?
TINA: Haven't you ever heard of mountaineers?

DAVID: I wish I had a rabbit so it could blow in my face.
LAURA: How come?
DAVID: Haven't you ever heard of people being saved by a hare's breath?

Long ago an old Indian was about to die, so he called for Geronimo and Fallen Rocks, the two strongest and most courageous braves in the tribe. The old Indian told them each to go and seek buffalo skins, and whoever got the most skins would be the new chief. About a month later Geronimo came back with two hundred pelts, but Fallen Rocks never returned. They searched for him carefully, but never was he found. Even now, as you drive through the Old West, you will see signs saying WATCH OUT FOR FALLEN ROCKS. . . .

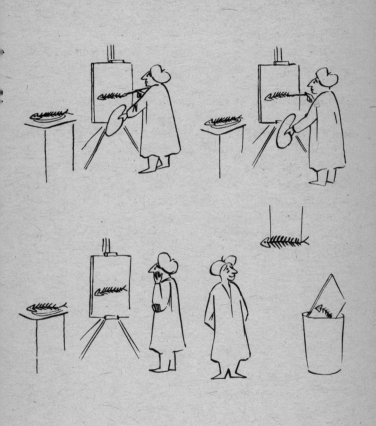

Jokes Elephants Tell

Our language is full of animal expressions. To name a few: "That's a howl," horsing around, squeal, "I roared," laugh like a hyena, pussyfooting, monkeyshines, aped, dodo, yak, parrot, social lion. We've taken these animals' antics and put them to use as words and expressions in our own vocabularies. An elephant friend of mine objects to this. He called me on the phone to tell me the following jokes. (He used a trunk line, of course.)

MOTHER OWL: I'm worried about Junior.
FATHER OWL: What is the matter with him?
MOTHER OWL: He doesn't give a hoot for anything.

A man went to a ranch to buy a horse, saw a beautiful pony, and asked what kind it was. "That's a palomino," said the rancher. "Well, any friend of yours is a friend of mine," replied the man.

This same man decided to buy the palomino. "Let me tell you first about him," said the rancher. "He was owned by a reverend, and if you want the horse to go, you say 'Good Lord,' and if you want the horse to stop you say 'Amen.'"

The buyer wanted to try the horse, so he mounted and said "Good Lord." The horse promptly moved out, and was soon galloping up the mountain. The rider was truly frightened and, forgetting the rancher's instructions, yelled "Good Lord, Good Lord," so of course the horse really raced along. Just as he was coming to the edge of the cliff, he yelled "Whoa, whoa," and when that didn't stop the horse, he suddenly remembered what the rancher had told him. "AMEN," he shouted, and the horse slid to a stop right on the brink. The man wiped his brow in relief, looked up to heaven, and said, "Good Lord."

A jeweler watched as a huge van pulled up outside his store. The back came down and an elephant walked out. It broke the window with a tusk, and then using his trunk like a vacuum cleaner sucked up all the jewelry. The elephant then got back in the van and it drove away. The jeweler, when he finally regained his senses, called the police. The detectives came, and he told them what happened. "Could you describe the elephant?" "An elephant is an elephant. How do you describe him?" asked the jeweler. "Well," said the policeman, "there are two kinds of elephants, African and Indian. The Indian elephant has smaller ears and is not so large as the African elephant." The jeweler answered, "I can't help you, he had a stocking pulled over his head."

A farmer couldn't tell his two horses apart, so he tried cutting the tail off one horse. This was no good because the tail grew right back. Then he cut the mane off the other horse. This didn't work either, because the mane grew back. Finally he measured them and found that the white horse was two inches taller than the black horse.

Two Boy Scouts on their first overnight hike had camped for the night. They were bitten by mosquitoes unmercifully. Finally they decided to cover themselves completely with a large blanket. Just then a firefly flew under the blanket. One scout sighed and said, "It's no use, they're coming after us with a lantern now."

And then there's the mad scientist who crossed a centipede with a parrot and ended up with a walkie-talkie.

MAG: What has four legs, is gray, and has a trunk?
BILL: An elephant?
MAG: No, a mouse on vacation.

A hunter shot a duck and it fell into the lake. Quickly he commanded his dog—a dog he had never worked with before—to retrieve the duck. The hound ran to the edge of the water, sniffed . . . and walked out onto the waters of the lake. The hunter was amazed. He shot another duck. It too fell into the lake. Again the hound walked out on the water to retrieve the duck before it sank. "At last," the hunter thought, "I have something to show to my friend who never lets anything disturb his cool." The next day the hunter suggested to his friend, Alex, that they go do a little duck hunting. His friend shot a duck, and it fell into the lake. The dog walked across the water to retrieve it and dropped it at the shooter's feet. The hunter asked his friend, "What do you think of my bird dog?" "Well. . . ." "Didn't you notice anything special about the dog?" insisted the hunter. "I noticed one thing," drawled his friend. "Your dog can't swim."

Did you hear about the dog with the cauliflower ear? He's a boxer, but not a very good one.

Three turtles were going on a picnic when they came across a can of soda. As they didn't have a can opener, they decided one of them would have to go home and get one.

None of them wanted to go, for fear the other two would have the picnic while he was gone. The first turtle argued that he was 700 years old and didn't have the strength to go back. The second turtle said he was 623 years old and therefore shouldn't have to make the trip. Thus the third turtle, being only 423 years old, was told to make the trip. But first he extracted a promise from the other two that they would not begin the picnic without him.

Seven years went by and he didn't return. The two turtles decided to keep waiting. Eleven years went by. He still didn't return. After fifteen years one turtle asked the other: "Don't you think we had better eat now?" "Yes, I think we should. It has been a long time." Just then out from behind a bush popped the third turtle, where he had been hiding all this time: "Ha, ha, I knew you were going to try to eat without me."

There is only one thing worse than raining cats and dogs, and that is hailing taxis.

The hippie called the fish hospital and asked to speak to the head sturgeon.

A lady out for a walk stopped to watch an organ grinder with his pet monkey. The monkey was grinding the organ and dancing at the same time. A passerby tossed the monkey a coin, which went rolling down the street. When the organ grinder ran after it, the monkey said to the lady, "He makes me dance and play music six days a week. On Sunday he lets people kiss me." "But does he know how well you can talk?" asked the lady. "No," said the monkey, "and please don't tell him, or he'll make me sing too!"

Two city boys found a pile of empty milk bottles behind a barn. "We've discovered a cow's nest," they shouted.

A Mustang and a Thunderbird crashed head on doing seventy miles per hour. When the police arrived, they found nothing but a pile of horseshoes and some chicken feathers.

There was a rumor that Ford recalled all its Mercurys. It found too high an incidence of tuna in them.

A man walked into a store and saw a horse behind the counter. He was speechless. Seeing his shock, the horse tried to reassure the man by saying, "It's all right, the cow sold me the place last week."

1ST HUNTER: Are you going to shoot that sea gull?
2ND HUNTER: No, it's your tern.

LITTLE BOY: I'll take a box of this birdseed.
STORE CLERK: How many birds do you have?
LITTLE BOY: None yet. I'm going to plant these seeds
  when I go home and grow some.

ED: Do you know why my white cows give more milk
  than my black cows?
BOB: You've got more white cows.

JACK: I've been riding sidesaddle since I've been three.
JOHN: Riding sidesaddle? That's the sissy way.
JACK: On an elephant?

  Then there was the boy who lighted a firecracker and
threw it. He got a big bang out of it when his retriever
brought it back to him.

BOB: Do you know where elephants are found?
SUE: No, where are they found?
BOB: Well, they're so big, they are seldom lost. . . .

STEPHEN: One mouse trap, please, and hurry. I have
  to catch a train.
LAUREN: What do you use for bait?

JON: My dog is a genius.
MAG: How come?
JON: I asked him what infinity minus infinity is, and
  he said nothing.

JAY: My cat swallowed a ball of wool.

SKIP: So what?

JAY: When the cat had kittens, they were born with sweaters on.

SKIP: That's some yarn.

JAY: Well, I'm a knit-wit.

Two mice were chatting in a laboratory: "And how are you getting on with your professor?" one asked the other. "Oh, excellently," he answered, "I have him thoroughly trained. Every time I ring the bell, he gives me food."

JEFF: I crossed a hyena with a parrot.

JOHN: Why?

JEFF: So I could ask what he was laughing about.

JAY: What do you get when you cross a pile of hay with a vampire?

SKIP: You get a bale o' Lugosi.

Two fellows were tired of their jobs. They decided to go into the trucking business hauling fruit. They bought a truck and drove it down to Georgia and bought watermelons for a dollar each. They then drove the truck to New York and sold them for a dollar each. That night they were counting their money. The first one said, "Charlie, I have two hundred dollars!" "Great!" Charlie replied. "But, Charlie, we started with two hundred dollars. We're doing something wrong!" "You're right. How stupid can we be?" Charlie said. "We need a bigger truck!"

Way-Out Jokes

These jokes are the zany type. The kind that could just possibly be true . . . until the ending. They're good practice for telling because they have completely unpredictable punch lines.

A store advertised a big sale to start at nine o'clock. Bikes for five dollars, sleds for one dollar—bargains galore. A line started to form about seven o'clock and was more than two blocks long by eight o'clock. One little fellow arrived about eight-thirty and slowly inched his way to the front of the line behind a big burly man. As he tried to get past him, the huge fellow yelled, "Get back to the end of the line." Frightened, the little fellow went back to the end of the line and again slowly inched forward until he was once more trying to get past the big fellow. Again he was told, "Get back to the end of the line." So again he went back to the end of the line. The third time he got behind the big guy he tried again. At this point the big guy grabbed him by his collar and yelled, "What's wrong with you? I'm first. What makes you think I'm going to let you get ahead of me?" The little guy looked straight at him and replied, "If you don't, I won't open the store!"

An usher noticed a man in the front row of the theater sprawled out with his feet on the stage. He went over and said, "Sir, you'll have to take your feet off the stage." The man replied 'AAAAGHHHH.'' The usher left and got the manager, who came down the aisle and said to the man, "We don't allow people to put their feet on the stage; please get them down or I will call the police." The man looked at him and said "AAAAGHHHH." The manager got a cop, who then told the man, "If you don't get your feet down, I'm taking you in. Where did you come from, anyway?" The man looked up and with great effort said, "From the balcony."

A kook drove up to the curb, parked his car, got out, locked all the doors, and then realized that he had left the keys inside. "Oh, rats! Let me think. How am I going to get into my car?" he said. "I'll have to break a window, that's what I'll do . . . but first I better call the garage." He called his garage and told the mechanic that he had locked the keys inside the car. "I'm wondering whether to break a window to get in," he said. "Don't break any window," said the garageman. "We have skeleton keys for every car. Stay where you are and I'll be right down to unlock the car for you." "All right," answered the kook, "but please, please, hurry. You see, it's starting to rain here, and I left the top down."

The title of biggest liar probably goes to a man who told people he was a diamond cutter. Really he mows the lawn at Shea Stadium.

A window cleaner was called in to give an estimate. The homeowner asked, "How much to clean the windows on the ground floor?" The window cleaner pulled out a pad, scribbled a minute, and replied, "Two dollars a window." "On the second floor?" asked the homeowner. The window cleaner again scribbled on the pad and answered, "One dollar and fifty cents a window." "And the basement?" "Five dollars a window," the cleaner answered. "Wait a minute," said the homeowner. "How come two dollars for the windows on the first floor, a buck and a half for the second floor, and you want five dollars for each of the basement windows?" Explained the window cleaner, "Don't you realize the size of the hole I have to dig to put the ladder in?"

KARYN: Why should you always drink from the side of the cup nearest you?
CINDY: Because if you drink from the other side you'll spill it all over yourself.

Once two hunters got lost in the forest. The first hunter said, "Now we must be calm." The second hunter agreed, "You're right. I read that if you are lost,

you should shoot three times into the air and someone will come and rescue you.'' So they did this, but nothing happened. And they did it again, and still no help came. They repeated this several times without results. Finally the first hunter said, ''What are we going to do now?'' And the second hunter replied, ''I don't know; we're almost out of arrows.''

DOCTOR: Have you carried out my instructions?
PATIENT: All but one. I'm not able to take that two-mile walk every morning that you suggested. I get too dizzy and wet.
DOCTOR: I don't understand, what do you mean?
PATIENT: I forgot to tell you—I'm a lighthouse keeper.

A doctor walked into his office, turned on his overhead lights, and found a man dangling from the light bulb. "What are you doing up there?" he asked. "I'm a light bulb" came the answer. "A what?" "A light bulb." At that the doctor unscrewed the man and marched him down the hall toward the door. On the way there they passed the janitor, who turned around and started following them. "Why are you following us?" asked the doctor. Replied the janitor: "What do you expect me to do? Work in the dark?"

BRIAN: Are you an only child?
STEVEN: No, I used to be twins.
BRIAN: When were you twins?
STEVEN: My father has a picture of me when I was two.

The steeple bells were tolling and tolling, and the townspeople were bewildered. Finally the mayor climbed into the tower and saw a man ringing the bells. "Why are you ringing the bells?" he asked. "Is this a special holiday for you?" "No." "Then," asked the mayor, "is someone being married?" "No" came the answer. "Then why," said the mayor again, "are the bells ringing?" "Because," replied the man, "I'm pulling on the rope."

A man walking along the road saw an Indian lying with his ear to the ground. He went over and listened. The Indian said, "Small wheels, Lincoln convertible, red, man driving, large dog beside him, Nevada license plate." The man was astounded. "You mean you can tell all that just by listening with your ear to the

ground?'' he asked. ''Ear to the ground, nothing,'' said
the Indian, ''that car ran over me.''

MAG: I left my watch upstairs.
PEN: Call it. Maybe it will run down.
MAG: It can't. We have a winding staircase.

Two shipwrecked sailors marooned on an isle in the
South Pacific were desperate after months of being
alone. One day they became hysterical with joy when
a bottle with a note in it washed up on their beach.
Eagerly they opened it, only to collapse with a groan.
''It's from us.''

A man walking down the street pulling one hundred yards of rope was approached by another man, who asked, "Why are you pulling all that rope?" "Well," answered the first man, "have you ever seen anyone pushing one hundred yards of rope?"

DAN: I keep seeing spots before my eyes.
ED: Have you seen a doctor?
DAN: No, just spots.

A man was invited to a costume party. He went to a store to get his costume. The manager had a beautiful pirate costume with cap, silk shirt, pants, boots and a real sword. The man asked, "How much?" "Twenty dollars," the clerk replied. "Too much. What's cheaper?" asked the customer. The costumer said, "I'll give you the cap, a sweat shirt, plain pants, a pair of boots and a rubber sword." "How much?" "Ten dollars." "Too much, what's cheaper?" asked the customer again. "Okay," said the salesman, "I'll give you the cap, the boots, a cardboard sword and sneakers." "How much?" "Five dollars." "Too much, what's cheaper?" By this time the costumer was a bit angry. "I have the perfect thing for you, sir," he said. "For two dollars I'll give you a broomstick and a can of red paint." "That sounds good," said the man, "but what do I do with that?" "You stick the broomstick in your mouth," answered the costumer, "pour the red paint all over your head, and you'll go as a jelly apple."

When a small anemic-looking man was hired as a bartender, the saloon owner gave him a word of warning: "Drop everything and run for cover if ever you hear that Big John is on his way to town." The man worked several weeks without incident. Then one day a cowhand rushed in shouting, "Big John is a'comin'," and knocked the unfortunate bartender to the floor in his hurry to get out. Before the bartender had a chance to recover, a giant of a man with a black bushy beard rode up to the saloon on a buffalo, using a rattlesnake for a whip. The man tore the doors off their hinges, flung the snake into a corner, and split the bar from end to end with one blow of his massive fist as he demanded a drink. The bartender nervously pushed a bottle at the man. He broke the neck off, downed the contents in one gulp, and turned to leave. Seeing that he wasn't hurting anyone, the bartender asked the man if he would like another drink. "Got no time," the man roared, "Big John's a'comin' to town."

The cowboy strode into the Last Chance Saloon yelling, "All right, all right, who's the wise guy? Who's the smart aleck that painted my horse green?" Silence. "Show yourself, if you dare," shouted the cowboy. The crowd gasped as a seven-foot-tall rough-looking character got up from the poker table and rested his hands on his gun handles. "I did it! What did you want to tell me?" The cowboy paled, swallowed the lump in his throat, and replied, "I thought you'd like to know the first coat is dry."

Two fellows traveling by plane were startled to hear the pilot announce, "Folks, our number one engine has developed some trouble. We'll make it, but there will be an hour's delay.'' Five minutes later the pilot announced, ''Our number two engine just quit. But don't worry, we'll make it. There will, however, be a two-hour delay.'' Ten minutes later he announced, ''Folks, our number three engine has gone out, we'll have a three-hour delay now.'' Two seconds later he came on again, ''Folks, we just lost our number four engine. . . .'' At this, one fellow turned to the other and said, ''Real great, now we'll be up here all day!''

A traveler went to a foreign country and arrived when the temperature was about one hundred and six degrees. As soon as he arrived at the hotel, he ordered lunch and some ice water. The waiter told him they had no ice. The traveler became very angry and asked for the manager. "How come this is supposed to be the finest hotel in the country and you have no ice?" he demanded to know. The manager replied, "I'm sorry, sir, but, you see, the man who had the formula died."

A well-known American big-game hunter flew to New Guinea for some hunting. After two weeks he was caught by a group of head shrinkers. They kept him prisoner for six months, and everyone thought he was dead. One day he managed to escape and made his way to civilization. At the first big town he reached, he placed a call to his wife in the States. "My dear," she cried, "it's a miracle. I surely thought you were dead. No one has ever escaped from the headhunters. How are you now?" "I'm all right," he said, "except that I have no clothes, only a loincloth. Would you please send me some clothes right away: three shirts, size sixteen; three pairs of socks, size eleven; one pair of shoes or sneakers, size ten; one pair of pants, size thirty-six; and oh, yes, I can use a hat here to protect my forehead." His wife said, "What size hat?" and he answered, "One and seven-eighths."

A visitor to a foreign country was to address the people. He was told they liked short speeches. As he stepped to the podium, he bowed to the palace and then to the audience. There was wild applause and cheers. Seeing this response, he decided to bow again to the palace and the audience. This time there were boos and catcalls. Puzzled, he turned and asked the prime minister, "What happened?" "I told you," said the prime minister, "they don't like long speeches."

Tongue Depressing

Doctors and scientists are in the news every day. They appear in jokes more than any other people in any other occupation. My doctor is really modern, he has a hi-fi stethoscope. Not only does he get my heartbeat, but it keeps time with Herb Alpert. So here goes with a whole case load of medical-type jokes.

A woman went to a doctor because she was concerned about her husband. He had complained about her cooking, so she bought a huge rabbit and on Monday gave him rabbit steak, Tuesday it was rabbit spare ribs, Wednesday rabbit's feet, Thursday rabbitburgers and Friday rabbit goulash. The doctor asked her, "What did he say on Friday?" "Nothing," she said, sobbing. "He just sat there and stared at me with those big pink eyes."

A sad and bedraggled man approached the most famous and expensive doctor in the city and admitted right off that he could not afford to pay his $75 fee. The doctor was feeling mellow, so he reduced his fee to $50. "But, Doctor," begged the sick man, "I have a wife and seven kids to support," and so the fee was brought down to $25. The man sighed. "For me that's food for my kids for a week." Finally the doctor said $15 and at the stricken look on the man's face said, "I know when I'm beat—five dollars. Only first, tell me this: I am known as the top doctor in the city, the most expensive one in fifty miles, why did you come to me?" "Because," answered the man emphatically, "where my health is concerned, *money* is no *object*."

The doctor was trying to help his new patient who was terribly upset. "You see, Doctor," he explained, "my problem is that I like shoes much better than I like boots." "That's no problem," answered the doctor, "most people like shoes better than boots. I myself like shoes better than boots." The patient was elated, "Really, Doc? How do you like them, fried or scrambled?"

A business executive put on so much weight that his doctor ordered him to go into the hospital. Whereupon he was immediately put on a very strict diet. When the man's office staff sent him a large basket of flowers, the executive acknowledged the gift with a note that said, "Thanks for the flowers; they were delicious."

The new tenant ran into the drugstore. "May I have

a box of rat poison, please?'' he asked. ''Certainly,'' answered the druggist. ''Do you want to take it with you?'' The tenant thought a minute and then said, ''No, I'll send the rats in after it.''

I went to a weight watchers' restaurant. While I was watching my weight, someone stole my coat.

The frightened patient ran into the doctor's office. ''Doc, Doc, help me. I was playing my harmonica and

I swallowed it." "Calm down," advised the doctor, "and don't worry. Think how bad it would be if you had been playing the piano."

A sailor limped into sick bay with a cast on his leg, and the doctor gave him a huge pill. Just then another sailor came in, and the doctor left the first patient. The sailor then limped over to the sink and choked down the pill. Then the doctor returned with a bucket and said, "Now drop the pill in the bucket and we'll soak your foot."

A farmer was putting a bucket into a well when a doctor came along and asked, "Is something wrong?" The farmer answered, "I'm just having a little trouble trying to get water from the well." The doctor said, "Let me show you how to do it." But the farmer answered, "Look, Doctor, you take care of the sick, and I'll take care of the well."

The very upset lady went to see her doctor. "Doctor, Doctor, my husband thinks he's a frigidaire. What it's doing to me—I haven't had a good night's sleep in weeks." The doctor was very kind and understanding, and told her that if she didn't stop worrying all night about her husband she would make herself sick. "You don't understand," the lady said, sobbing. "It's not his condition that's keeping me awake, it's the little light that goes on every time he opens his mouth."

Although she was hoarse, the woman protested vehemently against the doctor's bill. "You charged me five dollars," she said, "and all you did was paint my throat." "What did you want?" the doctor replied wearily. "Wallpaper?"

A man owns a youth formula and is manufacturing it. There are several rumors that this man is two hundred and eighty-two years old. A lady decided to see if this was true. She went up to his butler and asked if it was so, and the butler said, "I don't know, I've only been working for the man for one hundred and sixty-four years."

The crazy inventor was beside himself with glee until he discovered one small miscalculation. He had invented the world's most powerful glue but couldn't use it because he couldn't get the lid off the container. Then he invented a liquid that would dissolve anything it touched, only there was nothing he could put it in.

Two scientists sent a rocket into space to take a picture of the earth. When the rocket returned, one scientist said to the other: "Well, Stephen, how did the photo come out?" "Not so good, Jon," he answered. "Why not?" "Somebody moved."

The hysterical gardener rushed to his doctor's office. "Doc, Doc, you've got to help me. I've got a cabbage growing out of my ear." The doctor looked in astonishment and said, "How did this happen?" "I don't know," answered the gardener. "I planted carrots."

TINA: You never will believe this, but for months I've

believed I was a sick dachshund. My doctor has finally cured me.

MILLY: And you're completely cured now?

TINA: I sure am. Just feel my nose.

Oddballs
and Common Squares

Shakespeare said, "All the world's a stage," and you will find once the curtain goes up that there is a possible comedy playing in the everyday things about you. Let's take some of the following jokes that could have happened while you were on your way to the party—of course, no one will ever believe you, but they all will get a good laugh from the telling.

I saw a boy walking down the street this afternoon. He saw a man jumping up and down on a manhole cover yelling, "Seventy-seven, seventy-seven, seventy-seven. . . ." The lad walked over to him and asked, "Mister, why are you jumping up and down on the manhole cover yelling seventy-seven?" The man replied, "If you're so interested, why don't you go down the hole and I'll show you why?" The boy consented, lowered himself into the hole, and the man replaced the cover. As soon as he had done this, the man again began jumping up and down, except now he yelled, "Seventy-eight, seventy-eight, seventy-eight. . . ."

The hippie went to the doctor and told him he had swallowed five silver dollars about two years before. The doctor was puzzled and said, "If you swallowed them two years ago, why are you just coming to me now?" "It's this way, Doc," said the hippie, "I never needed the money before now."

Then I saw a hippie opening a can of sardines, and he said to his friend, "These sardines must be the dumbest creatures in the world. They crawled into the can, locked themselves in, and then left the key on the outside."

I watched this hippie swallow his watch by accident, and his friend said, "Man, does it hurt?" and the hippie answered, "Only when I wind it."

At a party I heard one hippie ask another, "What you chewing, man?" "Smart gum" came the answer. "The more you chew it, the smarter you get. I'm going to chew this five seconds longer and have a lot of great ideas." The first hippie was very impressed; he said, "You got any more, man?" The second hippie thought a minute and said, "I've got one piece left, but 'cause you're a special friend of mine, I'll sell it to you for ten dollars." "Here's the ten dollars," said the first hippie and popped the gum into his mouth. He chewed it a bit and said, "Man, this is A-OK. It tastes way out. You think I'll get smart from this? Funny, I don't feel any different. Man, I think it's a joke." The second hippie laughed and said, "See, you're smarter already."

Yesterday I heard about a hippie group that checked into this newly built motel. The desk clerk said, "I have three rooms for you, but my help is out, and you'll have to make your own beds." "That's okay," said the hippies, as they pulled out their hammers and nails.

I heard about this lady who was leaving California at the end of her vacation, and she said to the man next to her on the train, "I really loved San Jose the most." "Madam," said the man, "in California we pronounce the *J* as *H*. We say San Hosay. When were you there?" The lady thought a minute, and then answered, "In Hune and Huly."

And then the other day I heard a man telling about an incident that happened the night before. His bride had wakened him in terror, and he asked her what was wrong. She said she heard a mouse squeaking, and all the man could think of was did she want him to get up and oil it?

When I was in this lumber camp, I was watching two men sawing logs with a big saw. One man was big and the other was small. Another man came along and watched for a while as they sawed back and forth and back and forth, until he couldn't stand it any longer.

He went to the big lumberjack and grabbed him by the collar, saying, "If the little guy wants the saw so bad, let him have it."

Did I tell you how my mother gets me up every morning? She brings the cat to my room and throws it on my bed. And you better believe that always gets me up—because I sleep with my dog.

When I was waiting for my train, I heard someone ask the conductor, "Can I take this train to New Jersey?" and the conductor answered, "No, sir, it's too heavy."

My sister told me to close the windows because it

was cold outside. I think she is silly. If I close the windows, will it be warm outside?

Now I've got two questions to ask you. A man was locked up in a room with a piano, a calendar, and a bed. What did he live on, and how did he finally get out of the room? Give up? Here's the answer: He ate the dates of the calendar and drank from the springs in the bed. Then he used the keys of the piano to get out of the room.

And the second question is: How do you get out of a steel building with only a mirror and a table? Do you give up again? Here's my answer: You look in the mirror and see what you saw. You take the saw and cut the table in half. And since two halves make a whole, you can climb out of the hole.

Frantic Antics

Remember the one about the man who buys a ticket to the movie? He comes back a minute later and buys another ticket. Once again he returns and buys another ticket. The ticket taker asks him why he keeps buying tickets. He replies, "Every time I go in the usher takes my ticket and rips it up." People have been telling this joke for years. There are things that have not changed—like movie tickets—for years, in spite of science. Here are some gags that rely on the tried and true.

A man was introduced to a sword swallower who did his amazing routine in a circus. Not having seen a sword swallower before, the man asked him to demonstrate his act, whereupon the fellow swallowed some pins and needles. "But," protested the man, "those aren't swords—they're only needles and pins." "I know," was the reply, "but I'm on a diet."

I eat yeast and shoe polish every morning so I can rise and shine.

NEWSBOY: Mister, buy my last paper so I can go home?
MAN: Sure, son, how much?
NEWSBOY: Two hundred dollars. I live in Kansas.

I read the FBI has more than one million fingerprints in one room. I wish someone would tell my mother, 'cause I get yelled at for the same thing.

TIM: What should I wear with my yellow and red shoes, purple socks and green-checked pants?
JOHN: How about "hip" boots?

Two boys on a bicycle-built-for-two had a tough time getting up a steep hill. "I didn't think we would ever make it to the top," said the first one. "Yes, and it's a good thing I kept the brakes on, or we'd have rolled back down," said the second.

CAROL: I found a horseshoe.
PEGGY: Do you know what that means?
CAROL: Yes, some horse is running around in his stocking feet.

Once upon a time there were three men on their way home from work. The first man, passing a deserted old shack, saw a ten-dollar bill on the floor. He was about to pick it up when he heard a voice saying, "This is the voice of General Custer; touch that money and it

will be your doom." The man left the money and fled.

The second man spied the bill through the door, went in, and started to pick it up. Suddenly he too heard a voice saying, "This is the voice of General Custer; touch that money and it will be your doom." He too ran away.

Then the third man entered and was picking up the

bill when the voice said, "This is the voice of General Custer; touch that money and it will be your doom." And the man laughed and said, "This is the voice of Sitting Bull, and this ten dollars is going in my pocket."

JACK: Do you know that our school is like a TV show?
MIKE: You're kidding, how is that?
JACK: It's a regular *Laugh-In* at recess, but it's *Lost in Space* during math.

A man walked down the street and saw a little boy who was very tan. The man asked, "Are you tan from the sun?" "No," said the boy, "I'm John from the earth."

DAN: I think our school is haunted.
DOT: What makes you think that?
DAN: I always hear people talking about the "school spirit."

The movie star went to the fancy new store to buy a gown. She asked the manager what kind of clothes they sold. The manager answered, "Only the best, madam. Each gown cost eight thousand dollars, but each gown is totally different and takes six months to make. For your first one we will dip your body in wax and let the wax harden. This way we have your exact body measurements to fashion the gown to. Then we send to Rangoon for all of the wool from our special sheep. They weave it into cloth and ship it to England, where it is given a special dye job—any color you want, purple, perhaps, for your first. They will take a hundred purple plums, squeeze the juice from these fruit, and dye your gown the most beautiful purple you have ever seen. The buttons for decoration come from the beaks of egrets.''

The actress sighed. ''But I have a problem; I need my gown tomorrow.'' The clerk smiled and said, ''You've got it.''

ED: Did you hear about the fire at the shoe factory?
KEV: No, what happened?
ED: One hundred and fifty soles were lost.

Then there were these two cement mixers that got married, and now they have a little sidewalk running around their house.

A lady went to a big watch and clock sale that had been advertised as ''25 percent off.'' A week later she brought the watch she had bought back to the store, complaining that it lost a quarter of an hour every day. ''Of course it does, madam,'' said the clerk, ''didn't you read the ad? It said, 'twenty-five percent off.' ''

BOB: How come you're wearing your socks inside out?
TOM: Because there's a hole on the outside.

Ed got a pair of tennis shoes for Christmas and his friend Tom got a motor scooter. One day Ed challenged Tom to a race.

They're off—Tom zipped out in front at 20 mph. Ed caught up. Faster and faster they went —25 . . . 30 . . . 35 . . . 40 . . . 45 mph. Still Ed kept up. Tom couldn't believe it. He slammed on the gas and got his scooter up to 50 mph.

Finally, when he looked back, Ed wasn't to be seen. So Tom turned around and shortly came upon Ed lying in a ditch. "Ed," he cried, "what happened?" Moaned Ed, "Wow, have you ever had a blowout in a tennis shoe going fifty miles per hour?"

JACK: The laundry made a mistake and sent me the wrong shirt. The collar is so tight I can hardly breathe.
BILL: That's your shirt all right. But you've got your head through the buttonhole.

There was this little boy, bent on running away from home. He patted his puppy good-bye, stormed out into the night, and found it dark and cold; so he went back into the house to the dinner table at his usual seat. His parents ignored him quite icily. After a long time he said, "Well, I see you have the same old dog."

A beggar changed his pitch from ten cents for a cup of coffee to: "Will you give me twenty cents for a sandwich?" The pedestrian pondered a bit, then said, "I don't know, let me see the sandwich first."

BRIAN: What time is it?
DAVID: Three o'clock.
BRIAN: Oh, no!
DAVID: What's the matter, are you late?
BRIAN: Oh, it's not that. It's just that I've been asking

people the time all day, and everyone tells me something different.

ALASKAN: Our state is larger than yours.
TEXAN: It won't be when it melts.

There's a new story about the lady who wanted to be especially beautiful for a party. She teased her hair so much that it attacked her.

The truck drivers were having coffee at a trailer truck stop. They were each bragging about their trucks being bigger and faster than any other. The first driver said, "I made it from Albany to New York City in under four hours." Just then a third trucker came in. He sat down and ordered coffee. The counterman gave the newcomer his coffee and then went back to the first two truckers. "You guys brag a lot about how fast you are, but that's O'Driscoll, and he can top any tale you tell about speed in your trucks," he said. Just then a jet flew past, and at the noise O'Driscoll threw his coffee on the floor. "What's the matter?" asked the other truckers. "What's the matter?" stormed O'Driscoll. "For three days I've only stopped once a day for one cup of coffee, and each time that darned jet catches up to me."

MAG: Did you hear about the quartet that had sixteen legs?
MIA: How can that be? A quartet has only four people.
MAG: Yes, but the fourth one was a tenor.

A panhandler went up to the house. "Lady, I'm hungry, do you have anything for me to eat?" "Will you eat yesterday's soup?" "Yes." So the lady said, "Then come back tomorrow."

BOB: I see you've been hunting. Did you shoot that duck?

TOM: Yup, I shot him in the foot and the head at the same time.

BOB: How can you shoot a duck in the foot and the head at the same time?

TOM: Easy, he was scratching his head.

Steven passed a man's house and noticed that the yard had hundreds of old bathtubs in it. Everyday, for a month, he noticed that there were more and more. Then he noticed that the owner had apparently stopped adding to his collection. "How come you stopped collecting bathtubs?" he asked the property owner. "Well," the fellow answered, "I stopped when I got to nine hundred and ninety-nine." "Why didn't you make it an even thousand?" asked Steven. "Don't be ridiculous," answered the owner. "What would I do with one thousand old bathtubs?"

A man ran into the barbership. "You know that stuff you sold me for my hair—the hair restorer in the brown bottle?" he shouted to the barber. "Well, my wife used it on the furniture because she thought it was a new kind of furniture polish." "Don't worry," said the barber, "I've got more." "That's not my problem," screamed the man. "I want to know how much you charge to shave a piano."

An Englishman returned to his native land after becoming an American citizen. "What did you gain by changing citizenship?" asked his father. "For one thing," the son answered, "I won the Revolutionary War."

The silly lady was trying to buy a sweater for her cat. The clerk wanted to know the size, and the lady had no idea. The clerk said, "Bring your cat in and we'll try them on." But the lady answered, "I can't do that, I want it to be a surprise."

And here are words of wisdom: A cookie jar is a crummy place to keep your money.

And we all know what a board fence is, don't we? A board fence is a fence with nothing to do.

Daffy-Dillies

All I can tell you about the following jokes is that I think you will find them like peanuts and potato chips. I dare you to read just one!

The antique dealer was carrying a very valuable and rare grandfather's clock toward his client's house when a drunk lurched into him and knocked the clock to the ground. The dealer was furious and screamed, "Look what you've done to my clock." The drunk peered at the ruins on the ground, turned to the dealer, and said, "Why can't you carry a watch like everyone else?"

BOB: Did you hear about the dummy who threw himself on the floor?
ED: Nope.
BOB: He missed.

JACK: What is the opposite of sorrow?
BILL: Joy.
JACK: What is the opposite of misery?
BILL: Happiness.
JACK: And what is the opposite of woe?
BILL: Giddy-up.

There's an old saying at my school: If at first you don't succeed, well, you're about average.

MAG: Can you wear a henway with a lace dress?
PEN: Henway? What's a henway?
MAG: Oh, about two and a half pounds.

FATHER: You usually talk for at least an hour on the phone. But today you talked only for half an hour. What happened?
DAUGHTER: Wrong number.

Q. If Washington's wife went to Washington while Washington's washerwoman washed Washington's woollies, how many *w*'s in all?
A. None, there are only one *a* and two *l*'s in all.

"Mommy, Mommy, Billy says I have little white things in my head that bite!" cried Stacey. "Of course you do, silly," said Mommy, "they're called teeth."

LISA: Why did you cut a hole in your new umbrella?
RHONDA: So I could tell when it stops raining.

REAL-ESTATE AGENT: This house has no flaws.
PROSPECTIVE BUYER: What do we walk on, the walls?

My uncle died and left me two hundred clocks, and I've been busy ever since winding up the estate.

TOM: My sister tried to help my mother clean the house, so she put the Venetian blinds in the washing machine.
DEV: What happened?
TOM: Do you know anyone who could use eighty thousand toothpicks?

FRIEND: How's your new apartment coming?
BRIDE: Fine, we have one room all furnished from trading stamps.
FRIEND: That's great, but what about the other two rooms?
BRIDE: Possibly they're a problem—they're full of groceries.

The son of a farmer had come home from his first semester at college. At the dinner table that night he told his father he was studying trigonometry. "Trigonometry?" "Yes, Dad," he answered, "we learn formulas to help us solve problems. For instance, pi r squared. . . ." His father interrupted him, "Just a minute, son, any fool knows pie are not squared, pie are round."

LYNN: My father is up all night walking, walking, walking—he never sleeps.
PEGGY: Has he got insomnia?
LYNN: No, he's a night watchman.

TINA: My brother Brian chewed up my history book. Now he has hiccups all the time.
MILLIE: That just goes to show that history has a way of repeating itself.

MAG: I wish I could go to work in a candle factory.
DAVE: Why?
MAG: Because they work only on wick ends.

"My brother has so many troubles. He opened a stationery store and went bankrupt. He opened a gas station and went broke. He and another guy opened a luncheonette, and it went out of business in a month. Then he opened a bank." "That's great. What happened?" "He got five years."

BOB: A trampoline artist moved in today.
ED: What apartment is he in?
BOB: 3B and 4B.

MOM: Who was that on the phone?
SON: Oh, some lady who said it's long distance from London. I said it sure is.

Did you hear about the farmer who decided to wait until his son came home from college to put up a fence

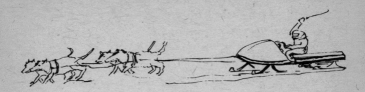

around his pasture? It was because in his last letter the son said he had made the college fencing team.

TEACHER: Lauren, make up a sentence using the word "climate."
LAUREN: The mountain was so big that I could not climate.

TEACHER: What's the formula for water?
STEPHEN: H, I, J, K, L, M, N, O.
TEACHER: That's not the formula I gave you.
STEPHEN: Yes, it is. You said it was H to O.

My sister gave herself a mudpack, and she looked great for days. Then the mud fell off.

OLD GRAD: I had the girls running in circles when I was in college.
WIFE: I never knew you were the campus hero.
OLD GRAD: What campus hero? I was the women's track coach.

There was an old woman who lived in a shoe—
She had so many children she didn't know what to do.

So she went to Thom McAn's and bought the other shoe.

BOB: You know my sister has an egg shampoo every
    night?
ED: What's so great about that?
BOB: You ever try to get a chicken to stand on your
    head?

Deedle, deedle dumpling, my son John,
  He went to bed with his stockings on.
One shoe off and one shoe on.
   That way he says it's easier to get dressed in the
morning.

CHILD: And what did you do when your ship sank?
SAILOR: Oh, I just grabbed a cake of soap and washed myself ashore.

JACK: How many controls do you have on your TV set?
MIKE: Six, most of the time—my father, my mother and my four sisters.

At any national park the most often repeated joke is this: What causes forest fires? Sometimes they are started by mountain ranges.

BABY ROCK: I'm nothing but a shy little pebble, will I get bigger?
MAMA ROCK: Speak up, and someday you'll be boulder.

SUZY: Did you hear what happened to John?
LAURA: No, what?
SUZY: He stepped in front of a moving train.
LAURA: How awful, was he badly hurt?
SUZY: No, the train was going backward.

The Tower of Pisa said to Big Ben, "You got the time?" Big Ben replied, "Yes, but not the inclination."

Mary had a little lamb, little lamb, little lamb.
Then she passed her plate again and had a little more.

JACK: Why did you put your toupee in your tuba?
BILL: I wanted to blow my top.

Mary had a little lamb, a little pork, a little ham. . . .

BILL: Want to hear a couple of lulus?
SKIP: Sure.
BILL: Lulu, lulu.

JACK: Have a peanut?
JAY: No, thank you. They're fattening.
JACK: How do you know?
JAY: Easy, did you ever see a skinny elephant?

Did you hear about the karate champ who opened his car window to signal for a left turn and chopped a Volkswagen in half?

RICK: If a man smashed a clock, could he be accused of killing time?
JERRY: Not if the clock struck first.

BOB: What's the difference between a gold filling, an expensive wedding, and a maple syrup bucket?
JIM: A gold filling is an inlay, an expensive wedding is an outlay, but why did you mention the maple syrup bucket?
BOB: To catch you, you sap!

There was this gentleman sitting next to a lady on a plane. The lady pointed to the word "Hawaii" and asked him how to pronounce it. "Havaii," he answered. "Thanks," said the lady. Replied the gentleman, "You're velcome."

STEVE: Yesterday I dropped an egg three stories without breaking it.
BRIAN: How could you do that?
STEVE: I dropped it four stories.

BOB: Did you know the bell ringer got caught in the rope?
ED: Yes, but he tol(le)d himself off, you ding-dong.

JACK: My ship was sunk, and I survived on a can of sardines for two weeks.

BILL: Tough break, but you were lucky you didn't fall off.

Did you hear the joke about the bed? It hasn't been made up yet.

Did you hear the joke about the knife? It's a killer.

Did you hear the joke about the roof? It's over your head.

MAGGIE: What is the best kind of fish to eat with peanut butter?
LAURIE: A jellyfish.

BOB: Where does the Lone Ranger take his garbage?
ED: To the dump—to the dump—to the dump-dump-dump.

TEACHER: What are the Great Plains?
WILLIAM: The 747's, of course.

MARY: John, I can't marry you, you're almost penniless.
JOHN: That's nothing, did you know that the Czar of Russia was Nicholas?

Clues Closet

Most gags are unexpected. To sharpen your imagination I have included what I call Mystery Quizzes. You read the paragraphs to your audience. They are to figure out the who, what and why. They are allowed to ask you questions that require a yes or no answer. I usually allow twenty questions. You will find these great at parties for team games, or you can use them on just one person, but let your imagination go. . . . (You will find the answers on page 94.)

1. A man has an appointment on the tenth floor of an office building. It is very important that he be there promptly. When he enters the elevator, it is empty. He looks in the lobby, and it is empty also. He then presses the button for the fifth floor. Why?

2. A woman has been found guilty of murder. The evidence was conclusive and she confessed to the crime.

When she comes up for sentencing, the judge has no choice but to free her. Why?

3. A man is running home and meets a masked man. He stops and then runs back to where he started. Why?

4. A man and his wife take a trip to Europe. While there, his wife meets with an accident and is killed. When he returns to the United States, the police arrest him based on evidence they uncovered. What was the evidence?

5. A man bought a rare coin imprinted with the date 1200 B.C. He knew it was a fraud. Why?

6. A man walks into a restaurant and asks for a glass of water. The counterman pulls out a gun and points it at him. The man says ''Thank you'' and walks out. Why?

7. A woman cleaning her sink put her diamond ring on the windowsill. When she discovered it missing, she told her husband. They both gave it up for lost, not stolen, and did not even bother looking for it. Why?

Answers

1. He was a midget and couldn't reach the tenth-floor button.
2. She was a Siamese twin.
3. It's a baseball game.
4. He had bought only one return-trip ticket, the other was a one-way ticket.

5. Too easy, how could they imprint the abbreviation "B.C." twelve hundred years before Christ was born?

6. The man had hiccups and the counterman scared them out of him by using the gun.

7. They were in a moving trailer.